The Sad Boy Who Got Help

by Ashton Lee Slattery

First published in 2020 by Success in Doing Publications

ISBN: 978-1-9160176-2-7

About the Author

This book is written by Ashton Lee Slattery, a 7-year-old boy from Ireland. Ashton is caring, kind and helpful, and he likes to share. He loves to see other people smile and hopes that this book will teach you that getting help is a good idea, if you want to feel happy.

Once upon a time Mommy and Ashton went to the park for a walk. It was a nice sunny Summer's day. The sky was blue and there was a warm breeze. Ashton was eating an ice cream and they felt very happy.

Suddenly, they heard someone crying.

They looked around to see where the

crying was coming from. There was a

boy sitting on a bench. He looked

upset.

Mommy and Ashton went over to the boy and asked him where his mom and dad were.

"I am lost," said the boy.

"Don't worry, we will help you! What does your mom look like? And what t-shirt is she wearing?" Ashton asked.

"My mom has red hair and she is wearing a pink shirt," the boy replied.

Ashton had an idea! "Let's work together everyone! Let's make a plan. Everything is possible when we do it together! How about we ring your mom's phone? She might answer!"

What is her phone number and name?

And what is your name? Mommy can

call her and tell her you are here!"

"Her number is 7769. My name is Alex

and my mom's name is Lily," said the

boy.

Ashton's Mommy rang the number

straight away and Ashton sat on the

bench beside Alex to wait.

"It's a good job you let us help you, Alex. You'd probably still be crying and upset, if you didn't. You know, it's good to get help, if you need it, because then we can solve the problem together. There's no point being upset and not doing something about it."

Alex agreed.

Then Mommy sat on the bench to wait with Ashton and Alex. She told Alex that his mom was on the way.

"Your mom was very worried about you, Alex," said Mommy.

Alex wiped the tears from his eyes.

"Oh, thank you very much for helping me. I feel happy now. I really appreciate your help."

"You're very welcome, Alex," said Ashton. "Would you like some ice-cream? When your mom gets here, we could buy you one. We could be friends."

"Oh, I'd love that!" Alex replied. "What's your name?"

"My name is Ashton."

"Oh, that's a nice name," said Alex.

Then Ashton jumped up, "I have another idea! Let's play catch until your mom gets here!"

"That's a great idea, Ashton, let's play!"

Ashton smiled and tagged Alex, "You're it!" Then Alex chased Ashton.

They became great friends that day, and they realised that getting help can make everyone happy!

THE END

Printed in Poland
by Amazon Fulfillment
Poland Sp. z o.o., Wrocław